MiG
DYNASTY

★ MIG DYNASTY

DAVID OLIVER

Airlife
England

Acknowledgements

The author would like to thank a number of photographers for their generous assistance with the production of this book, in particular Air Marshal A. A. Singh (Retd), Guido Buehlmann, Duncan Cubitt, Richard Gennis, Peter Gunti, Jan Jorgensen, Emil Pozar and Peter Steinemann.

This edition published in the UK in 1990
by Airlife Publishing Ltd.

British Library Cataloguing in Publication Data
Oliver, David, *1942-*
   MIG dynasty.
   1.   Mig aeroplanes, history
   I.   Title
   623.7463

   ISBN 1 85310 116 8 (Casebound)
   ISBN 1 85310 159 1 (Paperback)

Printed in Singapore by Kyodo Printing Co. (Singapore) Pte Ltd.

Airlife Publishing Ltd.

101 Longden Road, Shrewsbury SY3 9EB, England.

INTRODUCTION

The family of jet fighters produced by the Soviet Mikoyan-Gurevich design bureau (OKB) has remained the world's most widely used group of combat aircraft for more than forty years.

The remarkable partnership of Artem I. Mikoyan and Mikhail I. Gurevich was established as a direct result of Germany's invasion of the Soviet Union in 1940. Their first fighter design to achieve quantity production, the MiG-3, was delivered to front-line units only months after leaving the drawing board. Not surprisingly, it suffered from a number of major shortcomings. Nevertheless, more than 3,000 were produced and the fighter possessed the qualities that became hallmarks of all the Mikoyan-Gurevich design bureau aircraft: it was simple, sturdy and fast. The bureau's first jet fighter, the MiG-9 (NATO code-name *Fargo*), was virtually identical to the piston-engine fighter but powered by two captured German Jumo turbojets and made its maiden flight in April 1946.

Below: MiG-15 '23' is one of several *Fagots* performing on the US airshow circuit in the 1990s, nearly fifty years after the type's first flight.

A little over a year later, the aircraft that was to establish the MiG dynasty of formidable fighters took to the air for the first time. Benefiting from German wartime swept wing research and British jet engine technology, the MiG-15 alarmed the western powers when it first appeared in the skies over war-torn Korea. More than 8,000 *Fagots* — its inappropriate NATO code-name — were eventually to be produced by four countries serving with twenty-nine air forces.

Below: An immaculate LIM-6*bis*, a Polish-developed ground attack version of the MiG-17 with enlarged wing area, brake-chute fairing and unguided-rocket pods, still in use with Polish Fighter-Bomber Regiments in the early 1990s.

Produced in even larger numbers during a production span of twenty-two years was the MiG-17 *Fresco*, a redesigned *Fagot* powered by an afterburning development of the Soviet-built Rolls-Royce Nene. In the early 1970s, the MiG-17 achieved considerable combat successes in Egypt against Israeli jets, and over North Vietnam against US fighters. By 1953 the Mikoyan-Gurevich OKB had produced its first supersonic design, the twin-engined MiG-19 *Farmer* which was still being produced in China thirty years later.

The compact delta-winged MiG-21 *Fishbed* was a milestone in Soviet fighter design. First flown in June 1956,

it has established numerous world speed and height records, served with no less than forty-six nations, fired its guns and missiles in anger over three continents, and has had the longest front-line operational life of any combat aircraft in history. Over the years its engine power has increased by more than fifty per cent, some twenty variants have been produced and it has been built in greater numbers than any other jet fighter, with versions still leaving China's production lines.

The MiG-21 was a hard act to follow. It was the pinnacle of Mikoyan and Gurevich's long collaboration. Mikoyan died in December 1970, aged sixty-five, and Gurevich six years later.

During the late 1960s and early 1970s, a series of variable geometry multi-role fighter and ground attack aircraft, the MiG-23 and '27 respectively, both code-named *Flogger*, appeared. These were solid workman-like products from the OKB, now headed by Rostislav A. Belyakov, but it was the first flight of a new air superiority fighter in 1977 that caused as much interest in the West as the MiG-15 had thirty years earlier.

Below: An Indian Air Force MiG-21*bis Fishbed-L* seen against a dramatic Himalayan backdrop. More than 500 MiG-21s, known locally as 'Vikrams', have been delivered to the Indian Air Force since 1967 and still equip seven front line squadrons.

The MiG-29 *Fulcrum*, penned by Mikhail Waldenburg, who had been responsible for much of the detail design on the MiG-21, proved that the Soviet Union had made a quantam leap in fighter technology and produced a fighter to rival the West in the increasingly open post-*glasnost* market-place. Much of the MiG-29's success can be attributed to its powerful and efficient low bypass ratio Tumanskii turbofans. Inspired by captured German Jumo and BMW axial flow turbojets and UK-supplied Derwents and Nenes, S. K. Tumanskii subsequently designed the powerplants used in all Mikoyan-Gurevich fighters from the MiG-19 to the present day.

The Mikoyan-Gurevich design bureau is indisputably the world's most successful producer of combat aircraft, not only in its sheer volume of output, but because its aircraft are what they were designed to be; practical fighting machines, which have proved their worth in more conflicts than any other family of warplanes in history.

Opposite: An optional extra — distinctive intake cover fitted to a US-registered MiG-15 at Chino.

Below: The latest and best yet from the Mikoyan design bureau, the MiG-29 *Fulcrum* taxies in with its canopy slightly opened to give the pilot some welcome fresh air after a display which proved to be the highlight of Farnborough 1988.

Opposite: Two Chinese *Fagots* rebuilt to airworthy condition at Chino's 'MiG Alley' wearing Soviet markings and US register numbers.

Below: A growing number of MiGs have recently been 'captured' by the United States and have taken up residence in California. The instructions on the cockpit canopy cover identifies this MiG-15 (NATO code-name *Fagot*) seen after a rebuild at Chino, as having served with the Chinese Aviation of the People's Navy.

Opposite: The red-starred MiG-15s first appeared in the early 1950s and were soon locked in combat with US Sabres in the skies over Korea.

Below: US MiG-15s are allowed to fly at airshows under an 'experimental' category FAA certificate of airworthiness.

Opposite: Waiting in one of Chino's many aircraft dumps, this Chinese MiG-15 will eventually be rebuilt to fly again. In 1953 the US paid a defecting North Korean pilot $50,000 for its first MiG-15, nearly forty years on American private collectors pay five times that amount for an airworthy example.

Below: A Polish-built MiG-15 *Fagot* displayed in Chino's Planes of Fame museum in North Vietnamese Air Force markings.

Bottom: Another exhibit in North Vietnamese markings at Chino's Planes of Fame museum, this LIM-5, an ex-Polish Air Force MiG-17 (NATO code-name *Fresco*), a more powerful development of the MiG-15 which gave a good account of itself against more modern US fighters during the early years of the Vietnam conflict.

Opposite: Close-up of the MiG-15's formidable armament, a single 37 mm N-37 cannon and a pair of 23 mm NR-23 cannons.

Below: This ex-Polish *Fagot* is destined for the airshow circuit following a complete rebuild at Chino. Note the drop fuel tanks that no self-respecting MiG-15 would be seen in the air without.

Opposite: The Pakistan Air Force still flies a Chinese-built two-seat trainer version of the MiG-17 *Fresco*. The Shenyang FT-5 is based on the MiG-15UTI (NATO code-name *Midget*) trainer but features a larger rear instructor's cockpit.

Below: The advanced MiG-15 first hit the World's headlines when they attacked US B-29 bombers over North Korea in November 1950. This example, finished in a complicated North Korean camouflage, is displayed at Kbely in Czechoslovakia.

Opposite: Almost 10,000 MiG-15s were built in the Soviet Union, Poland, China, and Czechoslovakia where the type was known as the S-102.

Below: A Czech-built MiG-15*bis*, an S-103 displayed at Kbely, powered by a more powerful Klimov VK-1 used for ground support duties — note the non-standard underwing weapons pylon.

Opposite: A No 1 FCU Shenyang FT-5 advanced trainer seen over the scrub landscape typical of Northern Pakistan during a training sortie.

Below: Pakistan FT-5s, used as advanced trainers with the No 1 Fighter Conversion Unit (FCU) at Mianwali, are fitted with a single 23 mm cannon for gunnery training.

Opposite: Closely resembling the MiG-15, the MiG-17 *Fresco* which first flew in 1950 was a completely new design. Egypt, an early export customer used the type during the Six-Day War in the ground attack role. This MiG-17F *Fresco-C*, one of more than 120 delivered to Egypt, is used as an advanced trainer at the Egyptian Air Academy at Bilbeis.

Below: A rarely seen *Fresco-C*, this recently retired Cuban Air Force MiG-17F was used in the ground attack role until replaced by the MiG-23 *Flogger*.

Opposite: A mixed formation of three MiG-designs built in China and operated by the Pakistan Air Force. Nearest the camera-ship, a bare-metal Shenyang FT-5 of No 1 FCU, a two-seat FT-6 of No 25 Operational Conversion Unit finished in the latest two-tone grey camouflage, a bare-metal F-6 of No 14 Squadron and a second FT-5 of No 1 FCU in light grey finish.

Below: The enlarged rear airbrake of an ex-Polish MiG-17 *Fresco* displayed at the Chino Planes of Fame museum in California finished in the markings of the North Vietnamese Air Force, which also used the Chinese-built version known as the J-5.

Opposite: A Mianwali-based F-6 of No 25 OCU shows off its planform, twin-engine layout and three 30 mm NR-30 cannons, two in the wing-roots and one under the nose. The Shenyang is powered by two 7,165 lb thrust Wopen-6 turbojets, licence-built Soviet Tumanskii R-9BF-811s, which give it a respectable top speed of Mach 1.45 at 36,090 ft.

Below: China continued to produce licence-built versions of the MiG-19 (NATO code-name *Farmer*) until 1984, thirty-one years after the type's first flight. The MiG-19 was the First World's first operational supersonic fighter, beating America's F-100 Super Sabre into service by a few weeks. Pakistan remains a major operator of the the Chinese-MiG-19SF, the Shenyang F-6. Illustrated is a line-up of single- and two-seat F-6s operated by No 19 Air Superiority Squadron based at Marsoor.

Opposite: The sole FT-6 operated by No 26 'Spider' Squadron, two-seat version of the Chinese-built MiG-19, the F-6, sits with airbrakes drooping and drop tanks on the outer pylons on the apron at Peshawar.

Below: Some Pakistan Air Force Shenyang F-6s have been fitted with an additional ventral fuel tank in an effort to increase their limited endurance, as with this No 19 Squadron example at Marsoor.

Opposite: Three F-6s of No 15 'Cobra' Squadron based at Peshawar, carrying red-nosed 760 litre auxiliary tanks on the inner pylons, make a close formation turn at 5,000 ft near the Khyber Pass.

Below: A No 19 Squadron Shenyang F-6 landing at Marsoor trailing its braking-chute and ventral airbrake extended. Pakistan aircraft are fitted with Martin-Baker PKD Mk 10 zero-zero ejection seats and carry US Sidewinder air-to-air missiles.

Overleaf: A formation of four tankless Pakistan Air Force A-5Cs from No 7 'Bandits' Squadron fly over the desert with airbrakes extended, sporting yet more variations of the type's camouflage schemes.

Opposite: A camouflaged F-6 of No 19 Squadron carrying an unguided-rocket pod during live firing practice on the Marsoor weapons range.

Below: The Pakistan-designed belly tank restricts the use of the F-6's ventral airbrake.

Opposite: The Chinese Nanchung Q-5 (NATO code-name *Fantan*) incorporates some seventy-five per cent of the MiG-19, built under licence in China as the Shenyang F-6, including wings, rear fuselage, tailplane, wing-root guns, albeit 23 mm Type 2H cannons, and powerplants. The re-profiled nose, cheek air-intakes and rear-opening canopy allow more room for internal fuel, avionics and internal weapons bay. Some 120 of these ground attack aircraft have been purchased by Pakistan where it is known as the A-5C. This colourful example serves with No 16 'Panther' Squadron, the first unit to convert to the type in 1983, based at Peshawar.

Below: An A-5C belonging to No 26 'Black Spiders' Squadron well camouflaged against the tropical trees surrounding Peshawar Air Base.

Opposite: An East German MiG-21SPS *Fishbed-D* 'put out to grass' following the announcement of German reunification.

Below: All Pakistan Air Force A-5C aircraft are fitted with Western avionics and Martin-Baker zero-zero ejection seats. This No 16 'Panther' Squadron aircraft carries 760 litre drop tanks and wears a dark brown camouflage scheme in place of the more usual grey scheme. (See page 39).

Opposite: Known as the L17 in Yugoslavia, this latest version of the MiG-21*bis*, the *Fishbed-N*, has upgraded avionics, including an arrow-shaped ILS antenna (NATO code-name *Swift Rod*) fitted under the nose.

Below: Israel has 'acquired' several MiG-types including '007', a MiG-21F-13 *Fishbed-C* delivered by a defecting Iraqi pilot, Captain Monir Radfa on 16 August 1966. After evaluation by the Israeli Air Force (IDFAF) it was donated to the IDFAF Museum.

Opposite: Two of the latest Yugoslav Air Force MiG-21 variants, a MiG-21*bis Fishbed-L*, '210' in the foreground, and a MiG-21*bis*-K *Fishbed-N* '106' in the background, seen at Ljubljana in September 1989.

Bottom: A Yugoslav MiG-21*bis*-K *Fishbed-N* showing the tail warning radar fairing at the top of the fin, the prong IFF aerial and arrow-head ILS antenna above it, and the rear navigation light and trailing fuel vent below it. The dark green area at the top of the fin is the VHF/UHF aerial and, next to the Yugoslav star, the RWR magnetic detector fairing.

Below: Serbo-Croat graffiti — the mass of instructions, warnings and identifications stencilled on the rear of a Yugoslav MiG-21*bis*-K *Fishbed-N*.

Opposite: A Yugoslav *Fishbed-N* using the 8,000 kg thrust developed by its Tumanskii R-25-300 with maximum afterburner — almost twice the power of the YE-2, the MiG-21 prototype.

Below: A late series Yugoslav MiG-21PFM *Fishbed-F* taxies out for take-off with an external GP-9 twin-barrel 23 mm gun pack under the belly and UV-16-57 rocket pods on the underwing pylons.

Overleaf: A clean Yugoslav MiG-21PF *Fishbed-E* shows off its delta-wing planform, cylindrical fuselage, and no less than three extended airbrakes.

Opposite: The penultimate MiG-21 variant: a Yugoslav '21*bis Fishbed-L* seen in air-superiority grey taxying at Ljubljana in 1989. Note the lack of space between the pilot's helmet and the canopy.

Below: A selection of underwing stores carried by the Yugoslav MiG-21*bis*. Front to rear: 500 kg free-fall GP bomb, cluster-bomb dispenser, UV-16-57 rocket pod, outer pylon, and K-13A (NATO code-name AA-2 *Atoll*) air-to-air missile on the inner pylon.

Opposite: A twin-engine derivative of the MiG-21, the Ye-152A (NATO code-name *Flipper*) demonstrated at Tushino in July 1961, formed the basis for the latest Chinese Mikoyan-Gurevich design bureau-inspired multi-role fighter, the Shenyang F-811. After a protracted development, the F-8 prototype (NATO code-name *Finback*) first flew in 1984 and was to be the subject of a major avionics upgrade contract by the US Grumman Corporation before the programme was cancelled by President Bush, following the Beijung student massacre in 1989.

Below: The rear-opening *Finback* canopy, developed from that of the Nanching Q-5 *Fantan*, covers a cockpit that is almost 12 ft (3.70 m) above the ground.

Opposite: The Mikoyan-Gurevich OKB's most successful design to date — the MiG-21 *Fishbed*.

Below: The imposing Shenyang F-811 *Finback*, which retains the original MiG-21 delta wing design, is over 70 ft (21.5 m) in length, armed with two 23 mm twin-barrel cannon, four PL-2B infra-red air-to-air missiles (Sidewinder copies) and can carry up to 4,000 kg of ordnance on fuselage and wing pylons.

Opposite: This view of the 'British' MiG-21PF, G-BRAM, emphasises its exceptionally thin wing fitted with K-13 missile rails and when compared with the earlier MiG-21F (see page 64) its larger 800 mm main wheel tyres, enlarged radar cone housing the *Sapphire* radar and pitot head relocated above the nose. It also retained the front-hinged cockpit canopy and narrow-chord fin of the MiG-21F.

Below: The first MiG-21 to be placed on the British register, this ex-Hungarian Air Force early series MiG-21PF *Fishbed-D* was acquired by Aces High in 1989 and maintained in airworthy condition at the old Battle of Britain airfield at North Weald in Essex.

Opposite: In the final stages of a *Fishbed* rebuild at Reno, Nevada, in the summer of 1988. This ex-Hungarian Air Force MiG-21PF destined for a private collector, lacks tailplanes, 'bang' seat and cockpit wiring.

Below: The pilot forward view through the MiG-21PF's one-piece canopy is severely obstructed by the bulky radar display. It also lacks the glazed rear view panel of the MiG-21F.

Opposite: Another ex-Hungarian *Fishbed* far from home, 'this time a MiG-21F *Fishbed-C* acquired by the US Smithsonian Institute, Washington DC, in 1989 and displayed in North Vietnamese Air Force markings.

Below: The streamline 490 litre centreline drop tank was a standard fit to most early *Fishbed* variants to give them a reasonable endurance.

Opposite: A Finnish MiG-21*bis* taxies off the runway at Kuopio after an air defence sortie. Note the all-moving tailplane, main-wheel bulge over the wing, and the yellow and black striped anti-blast plate above the twin barrels of the semi-recessed 23 mm GSh-23L gun pack fitted under the fuselage.

Below: An immaculate MiG-21*bis Fishbed-L*, one of twenty-eight delivered to Finland in 1980, serves with *HavLv 31* at Kuopio. All wear the distinctive two-tone green camouflage schemes and 'MG-119' is seen here carrying three auxiliary drop tanks.

Overleaf: A Soviet *Fishbed-L* that visited Finland in 1974, '40' carried the legend '17th Congress of the Leninist Young Communists League of the Soviet Union' on its bare-metal finish.

Opposite: One of the few Eastern Bloc operational *Fishbeds* to wear a unit badge. This Polish Air Force MiG-21MF *Fishbed-J* at Poznan in August 1989, the first variant to be fitted with *Jay Bird* radar, wears the colourful knight in armour badge of the 7th Fighter Regiment based at Malbork in Northern Poland.

Below: The first *Fishbeds* to be seen in the West were MiG-21F-13 *Fishbed-E*s delivered to Finland in 1963. 'MG-47' of *HavLv 11* is seen on a visit to Uppsala in Sweden in August 1968 carrying a 490 litre drop tank on the centreline pylon. Note the glazed panel behind the cockpit and the single 30 mm NR-30 cannon fairing beneath it, and the small radar cone in the nose intake.

Overleaf: Vapour pours off the wings of this Hungarian Air Force MiG-21U *Mongol-B* two-seat trainer during a high-speed burner-turn.

Opposite: East and West meet over the Punjab: a HAL-built MiG-21*bis* named *Vikram* ('Brave') in formation with a Jaguar, local name *Shamsher* ('Sword'), of No 14 'Bison' Squadron.

Below: Three variants of the *Fishbed* have been operated by the Indian Air Force over the past quarter of a century. Seen here against the imposing backdrop, of the Himalayas is the latest in the line, a MiG-21*bis Fishbed-L*, built in India under licence by Hindustan Aeronautics Ltd (HAL) and fitted with a non-standard communications aerial in front of the cockpit.

Opposite: Silhouetted against the distant Himalayan peaks, this IAF *Vikram*, one of more than 800 MiG-21s acquired by India since the mid-1960s, will remain in front-line service well into the next century.

Below: The World's most widely used combat aircraft, the MiG-21 *Fishbed*. The camouflaged version shown here is an Indian Air Force MiG-21*bis* of No 21 Squadron, 'The Cobras', one of 200 manufactured in India under licence by Hindustan Aeronautics Ltd (HAL).

Opposite: The MiG-21*bis* pilot's forward view is severely restricted by the head-up display (HUD) and high coming. Note that the radar display has been repositioned compared with earlier variants. (See below).

Below: The snug conditions in the MiG-21PF cockpit, showing banks of radio, navaid and electronic warfare switches on the right-hand side, and the single red SK ejection-seat handle in the centre.

Opposite: A camouflaged Hungarian Air Force MiG-21PMFA *Fishbed-J* caught during a high-speed low-level run. The type has a maximum speed of Mach 2.0, 1,265 mph, at 35,000 ft.

Below: An Afghanistan Air Force MiG-21*bis Fishbed-L* flown to Pakistan in October 1989 by its defecting pilot. This was the fourth MiG-21 to arrive by the same method since 1986.

Opposite: The fully swept-back wings and all-moving tailplane of this Hungarian Air Force MiG-23MF *Flogger-B* are shown to advantage as it accelerates with full afterburner. Some eighty of these variable-geometry single-seat tactical fighters, which have maximum speed of Mach 2.35, 1,550 mph, equip two Hungarian Fighter Regiments and the type is currently the most common Warpac intercepter.

Below: Two generations of Mikoyan-Gurevich fighters built under licence for the IAF by HAL — a silver MiG-21MF Of No 30 'Vultures' Squadron with a camouflaged variable-geometry MiG-23MF *Rakshak* ('Guardian') of 223 Squadron with wings at forty-five degrees.

Bottom: Two generations of IAF air superiority fighters fly over the roof of the World — the dramatic Himalayas. A MiG-21*bis Vikram* in the foreground formates on a Mirage 2000H *Vajra* ('Thunderbolt'), forty of which were delivered from France in 1985.

Opposite: This East German Air Force MiG-23ML of *Jagdflieger-geschwader 9* 'Heinrich Rau' is based at Peenemunde on the Baltic. The *Flogger-G* is distinguished by its shorter dorsal fin, modified laser range finder housing under the nose, and bulged nose-wheel doors.

Below: A HAL-built MiG-23MF *Rakshak* with wings in the fully swept-back position. Its semi-recessed twin-barrel 23 mm GSh-23 cannon pack can be seen forward of the centreline R-60 *Aphid* air-to-air missiles (AAM) pylon, and underwing K-13A rails which carry medium-range R-23 *Apex* AAMs.

Opposite: An IAF *Shamsher* of No 5 'Tuskers' Squadron and a *Vikram* formate with yet another member of the MiG family, the MiG-23BN *Flogger-H*. Locally named *Vijay* ('Victory'), it is used by No 31 'Arrow Head' Squadron in the tactical air support role. This ground attack version of the *Rakshak* has its bulbous *High Lark* radar replaced with a 'Duck nose' giving improved forward visibility and containing a laser marked target-seeker and weapons system ranging radar. An 800-litre drop tank is carried on the centreline pylon.

Below: The latest Mikoyan design bureau ground attack aircraft, the MiG-27M is built under licence in India by HAL. The IAF *Flogger-J*, christened *Bahadur* ('Valiant'), has an advanced avionics suite which enables it to deliver a 4,000 kg weapons load with extreme accuracy. A warload of bombs, air-to-ground and air-to-air missiles is carried on four pylons, two under the forward fuselage and two under the wing glove. The small rear fuselage pylon carries an ECM jammer, while extra fire-power is provided by ventral six-barrel 23 mm rotary cannon. A total of 165 have been ordered by the IAF.

Opposite: A specially 'cleaned-up' version of the MiG-23ML tactical fighter (NATO code-name *Flogger-G*) seen on finals for Reims during a visit to France in September 1978 by a Soviet Air Force unit based at Kubinka, near Moscow. The lowered leading-edge slats, full span flaps, heavy-duty undercarriage and powerful landing light can be seen in this shot.

Below: An Indian MiG-23BN *Vijay* of No 10 'Winged Sword' Squadron landing at Amritsar trailing its brake-chute. The Squadron was the first of four IAF squadrons to convert to the type since 1981 when some 100 examples were ordered from the Soviet Union. Note both light and dark camouflage schemes applied to Indian *Vijays*. (See page 83).

Opposite: The export version of the *Flogger-B*, the MiG-23MF, equips two Regiments of Hungary's Magyar Legiero in the intercept and air-defence role.

Below: The first HAL-built MiG-23MF *Rakshak* entered service with the Indian Air Force in the tactical air support role in 1983.

Opposite: A low-level arrival flypast over Farnborough by the two Soviet *Fulcrums*, the single-seat MiG-29A on the left and the two-seat MiG-29UB on the right, showing the flush fitting auxiliary 1,500 litre fuel tanks carried between the two 18,600 lb thrust reheat Tumanskii R-33D turbofans and no underwing pylons.

Below: A line-up of Soviet Air Force MiG-21*bis Fishbed-L*s visiting Kuopio in Finland during August 1974. Finished in air superiority grey, '35' carries external fuel tanks on the outer pylons.

Overleaf: The two visiting Soviet *Fulcrums* on finals for Farnborough's runway 25 with landing light ablaze to open a new era in East-West relations.

Opposite: A pair of Soviet MiG-29 *Fulcrums* make a dramatic first appearance in British airspace *en route* to Farnborough on 30 August 1988, flanked by two RAF Tornado F.3s of No 5 Squadron.

Below: The graceful two-seat MiG-29UB with its long one-piece extended canopy and single 30 mm cannon installed in the left-hand wing-root.

Opposite: The difference in nose profiles of the *Fulcrum-B* trainer, foreground, and the single-seat *Fulcrum-A* is evident as they make a perfect formation landing at Farnborough.

Below: The instructor's seat in the rear cockpit of the MiG-29UB is only slightly elevated to improve forward visibility. For take-offs and landings with a pilot under instruction in the front seat, a periscope fitted in the canopy above the rear seat is used.

Opposite: One of the first MiG-29 *Fulcrums*, christened *Baaz* ('Falcon'), to be delivered to the Indian Air Force at Poona air base in December 1987, with its pitot-static boom, dynamic pressure probe and ISRT still under wraps.

Below: The latest air defence fighter designs from East and West parked next to each other on the Farnborough apron, the Panavia Tornado F.3 and the *Fulcrum-A* make an interesting comparison.

Opposite: Kvotchur holds the *Fulcrum-A* on a knife edge during his demonstration at Farnborough. The louvred 'gills' in the leading-edge root entensions (LERX) are auxiliary air intakes.

Below: With its nose in the air, Soviet test-pilot Anatoly Kvotchur touches down at Farnborough in the *Fulcrum-A* after another impressive flying display. The capable infra-red search and track (IRST) sensor and laser rangefinder can clearly be seen housed in a glass dome mounted ahead and offset to the right of the cockpit, as can the Mikoyan Design Bureau (OKB) logo on the engine intake.

Overleaf: A full afterburner turn with the *Fulcrum's* slab all-moving tailplane in evidence as Kvotchur pulls high 'g'. Note the four underwing pylons — production MiG-29s are fitted with six.

Opposite: The *Fulcrum* rotates into an impressive full afterburner climb-out from Farnborough's runway before the mainwheel doors have closed about to thrill the crowds with a polished display of power and manoeuvrability.

Below: The Soviet MiG-29UB *Fulcrum* leading its single-seat brother, is joined by a pair of Royal Air Force Tornado F.3 air defence intercepters of No 5 Squadron over a cloud-covered North Sea while flying from Moscow to Farnborough on 30 August 1988, in what must be the most unlikely formation of the 1980s.

Opposite: India became the first export customer for the MiG-29 which was offered at the fly-away price of US $11 million each. An initial order for forty single-seat and four two-seat *Fulcrums* was signed in 1985, with an option for HAL to licence-build a further 110, which has yet to be taken up.

Below: The first IAF unit to be equipped with the MiG-29 was No 47 'Archers' Squadron. One of its aircraft wearing the Squadron badge on the air intake is seen landing at Poona trailing its braking chute.

Opposite: A MiG-29 *Baaz* of No 47 'Archers' Squadron takes-off from Poona air base.

Below: The second of forty-four single-seat MiG-29s, KB702, to be delivered to the Indian Air Force, yet to be fitted with its underwing pylons, is prepared for a test flight at Hindustan Aeronautics Ltd facility at Nasik.

Opposite: The second Indian Air Force unit to convert to the MiG-29 *Baaz* was No 28 'First Supersonics' Squadron, which was also the first to fly the *Vikram* a quarter of a century earlier.

Below: The peaks of the Himalayas are the hunting ground for Indian Falcons. All IAF MiG-29s, including this *Baaz* belonging to No 28 Squadron, are finished in the Soviet-style two-tone grey camouflage.

Opposite: An unmarked and pylonless IAF MiG-29 lands at Poona after a training sortie with the aid of the large diameter cruciform braking chute.

Bottom: Rival state-of-the-art aerospace products from the Soviet Union and France are put through their paces in the mountains, with a No 7 'Battleaxes' Squadron *Vajra* trailing a No 28 'First Supersonics' Squadron *Baaz*.

Below: Close formation flying in a hostile environment. Two No 28 'First Supersonics' Squadron MiG-29s stick together as they weave their way through the towering peaks of the Himalayas which are picturesque in good weather but deadly when the clouds descend.

Overleaf: An IAF *Baaz* smokes-off the runway at Poona in an impressively short take-off with its leading-edge slats extended.

Opposite: Trailing smoke from its Tumanskii R-33D low bypass ratio turbofans, this MiG-29 of the No 47 'Archers' Squadron patrols the clear air over the Himalayas. Indian *Fulcrums* do not appear to be fitted with the *Odd Rods* IFF antennae on the nose.

Below: Taskayev, with Yuri Ermakov in the back-seat, taxies the *Fulcrum-B* back to its parking area at Le Bourget with its main intakes closed and trailing the braking chute, after performing a spectacular flying display only hours after his colleague Anatoly Kvotchur narrowly escaped death by ejecting from the single-seat *Fulcrum* following an engine failure at very low-level.

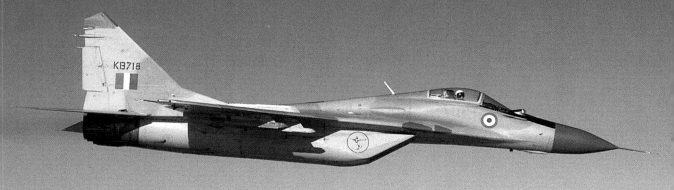

Opposite: The Soviet two-seat MiG-29UB *Fulcrum-B* is seen here through the heat-haze produced by the open jet exhausts, as pilot Roman Taskayev winds up the twin Tumanskii R-33D turbofans as he lines up for take-off at the 1989 Paris Air Salon.

Below: On 6 August 1989, two MiG-29s flew into US airspace from Siberia and were escorted to Elmendorf Air Force Base in Alaska by USAF F-16 Eagles to become the first Soviet fighters to land on American soil since the end of World War Two. The *Fulcrums* were *en route* to Abbotsford, British Columbia, to appear at Airshow Canada two days later. The single-seat MiG-29 seen here in Alaskan airspace flown by Roman Taskayev, carries two 800-litre drop tanks on underwing pylons plus the 1,500-litre centreline auxiliary fuel tank.

Opposite: The pilot of one of 20 single-seat and four two-seat East German Air Force MiG-29 *Fulcrums* operated by Jagdflieger-geschwader 3 'Wladimir Komarow' prepares for a dusk take-off from Preschen.

Bottom: Mikoyan Design Bureau (OKB) test-pilots Roman Taskayev, Anatoly Kvotchur (centre) and Yuri Ermakov pose for the press following their dramatic arrival in the two MiG-29 *Fulcrums* at Farnborough in August 1988.

Below: The then UK Secretary of State for Defence, George Younger, gets a privileged view of the single-seat *Fulcrum's* cockpit at Farnborough '88, albeit through the canopy.

Opposite: The first sixteen single-seat MiG-29 *Fulcrums*, locally designated L-18, were delivered in October 1987 to an air defence regiment based at Belgrade. The Soviet air-superiority fighter has a maximum speed of Mach 2.31, 1,520 mph, at 36,000 ft.

Below: Yugoslav *Fulcrums* are finished in Soviet-style two-tone grey camouflage, carry a 1,500 litre centreline drop tank and are fitted with six underwing pylons.

Opposite: Captain First Class Vlejo waves at the crowds from the rear seat of his MiG-29UB trailing the brake-chute and periscope extended during its landing run, after demonstrating the type for the first time publicly in Yugoslavia at Ljubljana in September 1989.

Below: The dielectric panel at the tip of this Yugolsav *Fulcrum's* tail fin is the UHF aerial, and the fairing beneath the tail navigation light is the Sirena tail warning radar. The stencilling on Yugoslav MiG-29s is in Russian, in contrast with that on MiG-21s which is in Serbo-Croat.

Opposite: One of a small number of two-seat MiG-29UB trainers acquired by the Yugoslav Air Force makes a short, full-flap take-off from Ljubljana into the evening haze.

Below: Prominent features of this L-18, a Yugoslav *Fulcrum*, are the huge, double skin variable exhaust nozzles, extended fin-roots which incorporate upward firing flare launchers, nosewheel mudguard and the wingtip radar warning receivers.

Opposite: Yugoslav groundcrew putting an L-18 under wraps. Note the shaped red covers over the IRST ball, the AoA sensor on the side of the nose, and the *Odd Rods* and UHF aerial under the nose. Old-fashioned canvas is used to cover the Fulcrum's NO193 *Flash Dance* radar.

Below: This close-up of a Yugoslav MiG-29 shows the single 30 mm cannon port and flash guard in the wing-root, the head-up-display (HUD), the infra-red search and track (IRST) laser rangefinder dome and *Odd Rods* ahead of the canopy, a temperature probe beneath it, and the knife-blade angle of attack (AoA) sensor forward of it.

Opposite: Red-starred fin of a USN Aggressor F-16N showing the tail radar warning antenna at the tip, braking chute fairing at the base, and the Fighting Falcon's fully variable exhaust nozzle, make an interesting comparison with the real thing — a MiG-29 *Fulcrum* on page 122.

Below: The ultimate 'Aggressor' — a US Navy F-16N Fighting Falcon. Three squadrons of 'MiG-29 simulators', stripped-down F-16Cs with a General Electric F110 turbofan wearing Soviet-style camouflage schemes, serial numbers and Red Stars, are used by the USN in the adversary role. *'Red 23'* of VF-43 'Challengers' flies dissimilar air combat training (DACT) missions with USN Tomcats at NAS Oceana, Virginia.

Opposite: Resplendent in *Fulcrum*-grey camouflage, including the ladder, and 'hammer and sickle' intake cover, this United States Air Force F-16C was flown by the 64th Aggressor Squadron (AS) of the 57th Fighter Weapons Wing (FWW) at Nellis AFB in Nevada, prior to the USAF's Aggressor force de-activation early in 1990.

Below: Several Israeli IAI Kfirs were used until recently by the US Navy as MiG-23 *Flogger* simulators. Designated the F-21A, this Kfir, Israeli for 'Lion Cub', was operated by VF-43 'Challengers' at NAS Oceana.

Opposite: Carrying an inert Sidewinder AAM of the port wingtip and wearing an appropriate 'snake' camouflage, another F-16C of the 64th AS lands at Nellis.

Below: UK-based F-16C Aggressors of the 527th AS, based at RAF Bentwaters, differed from those at Nellis by wearing the normal USAFE grey camouflage scheme and Soviet-style serials behind the cockpit instead of on the intake.

Opposite: On finals for Nellis AFB, a 'gray' 64th AS F-16C carrying on a wingtip an Air Combat Manoeuvring Instrumentation (ACMI) system pod and recording pod, and a centreline jammer. Call-signs used by the Aggressors included *MiG*; *Ivan*; *Fitter* and *Flogger*.

Below: Contrasting colour schemes applied to two US Navy Aggressors of VF-127 'Cylons'; in the foreground a Northrop F-5E Tiger II and in the background a two-seat A-4J Skyhawk used by adversary pilots under training.

Opposite: Frozen in the desert air overlooking the Nevada mountains, this 'blue' F-5E Aggressor became a gate guardian at Nellis AFB following its retirement from the 57th FWW at the end of 1988.

Below: The effectiveness of the 'snake' scheme worn by *Red 72* can be appreciated as it taxies out at Nellis against the backdrop of Sunrise Mountain.

Opposite: The latest operational versions of the Soviet Union Air Force's (VVS) MiG-29s were seen when the type made a second visit to Finland in August 1989. Back-tracking on Kuopio's runway is one of the five *Fulcrums* that appeared in an airshow at Finland's MiG-21 base. Note the pilot has already taken his helmet off.

Below: A close relative of the F-5, the two-seat T-38A Talon was used in the adversary role at the USAF Training Command. The pair illustrated belong to the 479th Tactical Training Wing (TTW) based at Hollman AFB, New Mexico, with the 'City of Alamogordo' in the foreground.

Opposite: A US Navy F-16N Aggressor of VF-45 'Blackbirds' over the Gulf of Mexico during a DACT mission from NAS Key West in Florida.

Below: A multi-colour line-up of UK-based USAFE F-5E Aggressors. The Tiger IIs, used as MiG-21 simulators, were operated by the 527th AS at RAF Alconbury from 1966 to 1988 before being replaced by the more capable F-16C.

Overleaf: One of the more bizarre Aggressor colour schemes, a cross between 'lizard' and 'snake', adorns this UK-based Tiger II winding-up its twin 5,000 lb thrust GE J85-GE-21 turbojets at Alconbury.

Opposite: With a new generation of sophisticated Soviet types, such as the *Fulcrum*, entering service in the 1980s, the GD F-16 Fighting Falcon replaced the F-5 in USAF and USAFE Aggressor squadrons. In 1988, the UK-based 527th AS moved to RAF Bentwaters with its new F-16Cs.

Below: The 'sky' camouflage applied to this VF-45 A-4E Skyhawk Aggressor works well as it flies over the warm Gulf waters. The veteran A-4 simulates the even more veteran but agile MiG-17 *Fresco*.

Bottom: A *Flogger* look-alike, this US Marine Corps IAI F-21A Kfir Aggressor is one of thirteen Israeli Mirage developments flown from MCAS Yuma in Arizona by VMFT-401 Snipers. *Red 13*, carrying an underwing ACMI pod and a centreline drop tank under the wing, wears the standard IDFAF desert paint scheme.